To my three little girls, L, E & T.
May you always love and respect yourselves.

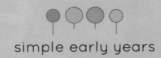

simple early years

A Simple Early Years Book
First published 2022 by Simple Early Years Children's Books
an imprint of Grivante Press
Lansdowne Road, Tunbridge Wells, Kent, TN1 2NJ
www.simpleearlyyears.com

ISBN 979-8-3728-6585-3

A CIP catalogue record for this book is available from the British Library

Printed in United Kingdom

Pocket POSITIVES for little rockets

Written by
Charlotte Lucas

Illustrated by
Kristina Shichkova

Before you came into this world
I looked up at the stars above
and chose you my little Love.
You have been given the gift of life.
With that you must live everyday,
for you alone are the shining star
that lights your way.
Be kind to yourself and love you for YOU!
For you are special in all you do!
Say these lines everyday
it will help you on your way...

I AM GROWING

Always, like a TREE
with deep ROOTS.

I will grow TALL and STRONG.

From these little seeds
grow MIGHTY trees

I AM JOY

JOY is APPRECIATING
how great your life is,
Choose joy in your day.
Then go on your merry way.

I AM UNIQUE

We are all different but
EQUAL
There is no one better to
be me than ME!
Be the best version of YOU

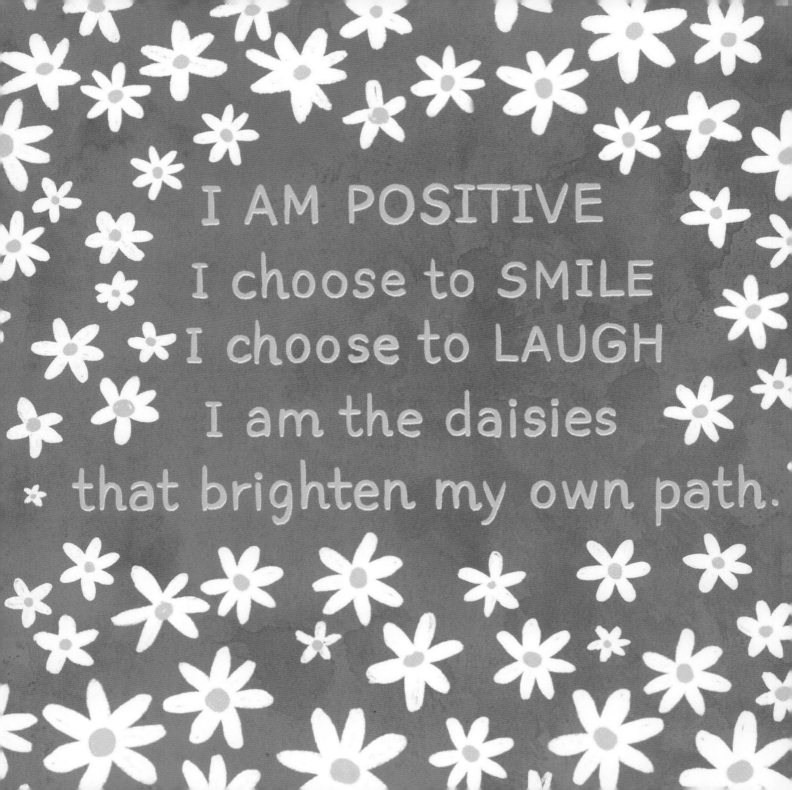

I AM POSITIVE

I choose to SMILE

I choose to LAUGH

I am the daisies

that brighten my own path.

I AM

Love is all

Your love fills my heart

Love can send me

Love is

LOVE

around me.

with JOYFUL BLISS

into the abyss

everything.

I AM HAPPINESS
when the rain falls,
don't be sad be GLAD!
For the flowers
drink the water below,
which helps them GROW.

I am brave

When I bend I will not break
I will stand STRONG and TALL
For my friends for them all.

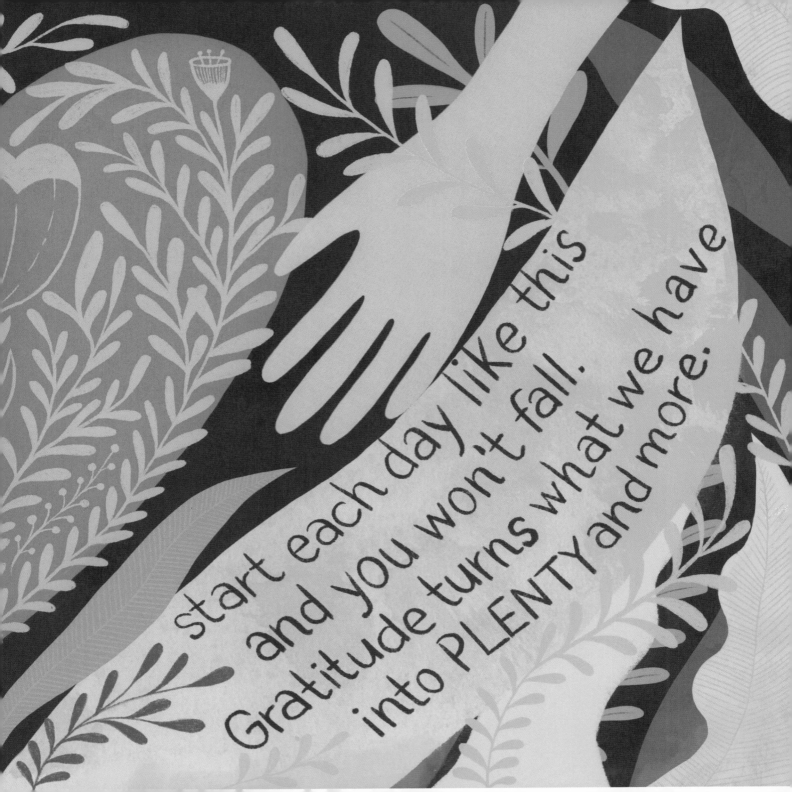

I AM AN ENVIRONMENTALIST

A BEAUTIFUL world starts with ME

MOTHER EARTH protects me

and so I shall PROTECT her.

With my actions I will help

SAVE THE WORLD!

I am my Dreams
I can do anything
I put my mind to,
Dreaming BIG
because only I have the power
to make them come true.

Now your turn ...

I am

I am

I am

I am

I am

I am

__ __ __ __ __ __ __ __ __ __

(NAME HERE)

ABOUT THE AUTHOR

Charlotte Lucas is the founder of Simple Early Years™, the provider of creative educational resources for children.

Born in a small town on the north island of New Zealand, she studied Early Years and Human Development with the ambition of being a teacher. That ambition led her to London, England, and following a decade working in the field, she met Alan and became parent to three girls. Having three under-fives calls for some serious coordination and entertainment ideas, thus Simple Early Years™ was formed with the aim to help inspire and enable others with the same needs.

Charlotte's ethos is 'When children develop their self-belief, learn to manage their minds and regulate their emotions, they become confident and happy. Early years are the time to start - when you know how, it really is quite simple'.

Follow Simple Early Years™ on Instagram